Illustrator:
José L. Tapia

Editorial Project Manager:
Evan D. Forbes, M.S. Ed.

Editor
Dona Herweck Rice

Editor-in-Chief:
Sharon Coan, M.S. Ed.

Creative Director:
Elayne Roberts

Cover Artist:
Keith Vasconcelles

Product Manager:
Phil Garcia

Imaging:
Rick Chacón

Publishers:
Rachelle Cracchiolo, M.S. Ed.
Mary Dupuy Smith, M.S. Ed.

Critical Thinking Activities

Brain Teasers

Grade 5

Author:

Carol Eichel

Teacher Created Materials, Inc.
6421 Industry Way
Westminster, CA 92683

www.teachercreated.com

©1995 Teacher Created Materials, Inc.
Reprinted, 1999
Made in U.S.A.
ISBN-1-55734-511-2

TABLE OF CONTENTS

INTRODUCTION

Brain Teasers provides ways to exercise and develop brain power! Each page stands alone and can be used as a quick and easy filler activity. The pages can be distributed to students as individual worksheets or made into transparencies for presentation to the entire class at once. The book is divided into sections so the teacher can find activities related to a subject being taught or to a particular student's needs. The activities are especially useful in helping students develop:

- Logic and other critical thinking skills.

- Creative thinking skills.

- Research skills.

- Spelling skills.

- General vocabulary skills.

FAMOUS PAIRS

Name the famous counterparts.

Superman and _____

Antony and _____

Ozzie and _____

Hansel and _____

Orville and _____

Laurel and _____

Robin Hood and _____

Lewis and _____

Samson and _____

Romeo and _____

Blondie and _____

Abbott and _____

Calvin and _____

Sylvester and _____

Laverne and _____

3

WORD TWINS

Write the other half of each phrase below.

1. Lost and _____
2. Back and _____
3. Good and _____
4. Far and _____
5. Black and _____
6. Meat and _____
7. Bacon and _____
8. Hammer and _____
9. Aches and _____
10. Mix and _____
11. Pride and _____
12. Prim and _____
13. Hand and _____
14. Macaroni and _____
15. Bread and _____
16. Liver and _____
17. Come and _____
18. Pins and _____
19. Touch and _____
20. Right and _____

21. Left and _____
22. Sing and _____
23. Cup and _____
24. Up and _____
25. Safe and _____
26. Nuts and _____
27. Thick and _____
28. Read and _____
29. Pork and _____
30. Knife and _____
31. Yes and _____
32. Soap and _____
33. Live and _____
34. Stop and _____
35. Salt and _____
36. Sticks and _____
37. Toss and _____
38. High and _____
39. Now and _____
40. Tooth and _____

NAME THREE

Name three items that belong to each category.

1. Things that are red _____

2. Things that swim _____

3. Things to do when you are ill _____

4. Months that have 30 days _____

5. Four-legged animals _____

6. Flowers _____

7. Kinds of clouds _____

8. Scary things _____

9. Reference books _____

10. Citrus fruits _____

11. Candies with nuts _____

12. American League teams _____

13. Places people live _____

14. Elements (chemical) _____

15. Things that give off heat _____

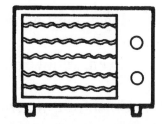

WHICH ONE DOES NOT BELONG?

One of the four words in each group below does not belong with the other three. Circle the one that does not fit. Then, explain what the others have in common. An example has been done for you.

Australia, South America, Europe, (France) : They are continents.

1. Giggle, chuckle, laugh, cry   _____

2. Dark clouds, rain, sun, lightning   _____

3. Carnation, tomato, daisy, rose   _____

4. Math, encyclopedia, thesaurus, dictionary   _____

5. Mother, nephew, aunt, niece   _____

6. Piglet, sow, boar, gosling   _____

7. Liver, blood, heart, kidney   _____

8. Washington, Oregon, Oklahoma, California   _____

9. Pig, chicken, cow, horse   _____

10. Relish, hamburgers, mustard, ketchup   _____

11. Dodgers, White Sox, Bears, Orioles   _____

12. Marker, eraser, chalk, pen   _____

13. Bagel, muffin, bread, margarine   _____

14. Green, yellow, blue, red   _____

15. Grapefruit, watermelon, orange, lemon   _____

BASEBALL LINEUP

All nine players on the Panther baseball team are sitting on the bench in their batting order. Using the clues below, find their batting order.

1. Jeff is batting fifth, and David will bat before Carlos.

2. Jordi sits between David and Greg, and Andrew is to the right of Jeff.

3. Greg bats after Jordi but before Andrew.

4. Phil sits next to Carlos.

5. Carlos and Tom are at each end of the bench.

	1	2	3	4	5	6	7	8	9
Jeff									
David									
Carlos									
Jordi									
Greg									
Andrew									
Phil									
Tom									
Luis									

BARNUM AND BAILEY CIRCUS

Brooke, Becky, Alexis, and Lindsey went to the circus last Saturday. Each girl saw her favorite animal and ate her favorite food. From the clues given, determine each girl's favorite animal and food.

1. Becky loves the elephants but does not like popcorn or taffy.

2. Alexis is afraid of the lions.

3. The girl who loves lions does not eat taffy or ice cream, but the girl who eats a snowcone loves the monkeys.

4. Brooke enjoys any flavor of taffy.

	Lions	Elephants	Monkeys	Horses	Taffy	Popcorn	Ice cream	Snowcone
Becky								
Alexis								
Lindsey								
Brooke								

8

TEACHERS' MEETING

Recently, teachers from all over the United States met together in Chicago for a national meeting. Four of the teachers decided to continue the day's discussion over dinner. From the clues below, determine the subject taught by each teacher, what state each teacher is from, and what type of food each teacher ordered.

1. Illinois is the home of the math teacher.

2. Mrs. Jackson teaches geography but doesn't live in Nevada.

3. The English teacher comes from Wisconsin and loves Italian.

4. Mrs. Jackson did not order Chinese or Italian.

5. Ms. Snow lives in Illinois but doesn't teach English and didn't order Italian.

6. Mr. Hunter loves Mexican food but isn't from Wisconsin.

	Ms. Snow	Mr. Hunter	Mr. Wong	Mrs. Jackson
Wisconsin				
Nevada				
California				
Illinois				
Geography				
Math				
English				
Science				
Italian				
Chinese				
American				
Mexican				

GETTING FIT

David, Tom, Rick, and Roger have each found a way to keep fit: jogging, bicycling, golfing, and swimming. They each spend different amounts of time doing these athletic exercises. Using the clues below, determine each man's activity and the time he spends at it each day.

1. Roger spends more time exercising than does Tom or Rick, but he does not golf or bike.

2. David jogs.

3. Rick exercises for 45 minutes.

4. Tom spends less time at his activity than the person who golfs but more time than David.

	David	Tom	Rick	Roger
jogging				
bicycling				
golfing				
swimming				
15 minutes				
30 minutes				
45 minutes				
60 minutes				

PALINDROME WORD FIND

Palindromes are words, phrases, sentences, or numbers that read the same forwards and backwards. Two examples are *121* and *Anna.* See how many palindromes you can find in this puzzle. (There are 32 words in all.)

```
S  J  B  L  A  D  B  B  U  O  F  M  B  E  W  E  Z  C
L  O  P  E  A  C  O  I  D  L  N  U  N  T  R  H  N  H
E  C  O  E  C  B  Q  O  B  J  T  M  M  O  E  A  B  T
V  T  M  Y  E  P  D  K  P  K  N  L  T  A  O  N  P  B
E  O  O  L  Z  P  M  H  E  V  E  I  Q  D  D  N  E  A
L  O  W  T  U  X  N  A  T  S  Q  M  T  H  I  A  E  T
A  T  J  P  S  R  N  U  Z  K  A  R  S  T  H  M  X
N  A  D  D  B  D  R  R  Z  P  L  J  O  O  U  Q  O  J
J  Z  S  O  Z  I  A  T  K  W  O  H  A  L  T  R  X  O
D  E  E  D  M  G  D  A  B  S  S  P  W  O  C  O  L  T
B  Y  A  O  A  M  A  G  K  V  A  L  P  S  I  K  R  T
T  E  R  A  N  S  R  G  W  D  G  Z  F  R  V  G  V  O
E  A  R  K  N  L  S  L  O  I  A  L  U  P  I  K  M  O
R  E  P  A  P  E  R  U  W  D  S  N  I  O  C  M  O  T
R  K  H  Y  S  X  P  S  N  J  E  O  N  T  E  R  M  G
E  O  K  A  F  O  I  U  D  U  D  M  B  A  C  E  B  I
T  H  A  K  D  J  M  N  X  R  G  H  E  W  C  A  B  T
S  E  E  S  U  N  X  W  O  A  L  S  K  A  G  Z  P  O
```

CARS, CARS, AND MORE CARS

Find and circle the following cars: Accord, BMW, Camaro, Civic, Corvette, Cougar, Cutlass, Firebird, Granada, Grand Am, Grand Prix, Gremlin, Impala, Jaguar, Javelin, Lamborghini, LeBaron, Malibu, Maverick, Mustang, Nova, Omni, Pacer, Pinto, Porsche, Regal, Skylark, Thunderbird, and Volkswagen.

```
S M U K S B V C L J O V N M D J E P D
K J U E W K I O W C T Q Z R K A G I O
B A X S J O V U B M X J I W D V R N M
M G K G T R E G A L G B A U I E A T N
W U J B R A S A Y R E H M N W L N O I
B A S X C D N R N R Y N I K L I D C P
A R F T J C M G I K I H R L E N A U A
K H X H A D P F S L G A A W B U M T C
B U L U L N V O M R L A C B A H F L E
T P U N L P G E O Y A O V V R P S A R
P L H D W Z R B K S R V X O O Z P S U
O F H E M G M S A A C I L L N T Z S B
R N O R H A R M M I D H B K T X S U C
S P J B L C L A V E W O E S V W T B J
C D A I V C C I N O Z M N W T H P S R
H C P R I O C B B A I M P A L A R U Y
E B E D R R Z P T U D M C G K N N T J
S K O R S D J M W X M A V E R I C K L
C O R V E T T E E Z G R A N D P R I X
```

WHAT IS THE QUESTION?

Write a question for each of the following answers.

1. Jupiter _____

    _____

2. Cherry pie _____

    _____

3. The zoo _____

    _____

4. 64 _____

    _____

5. Johann Bach _____

    _____

6. Yes _____

    _____

7. A tornado _____

    _____

8. 100 _____

    _____

9. The Indianapolis 500 _____

    _____

10. No _____

    _____

HIDDEN MEANINGS

Explain the meaning of each box.

F Ⅎ A A C Ɔ E Ǝ	**man** ————— **board**	LE VEL
1. ~~face n face~~	2. _____	3. _____

wear
—————
long
	d
	d e e r
	  e
	  r
		HEAD
		—————
		HEELS

4. ~~long underwear~~	5. ~~deer crossing~~	6. _____
businesspleasure	coORDERurt	N W O T
7. _____	8. _____	9. _____
Ban ana	0 ————— B.S. M.A. Ph.D.	sota
10. _____	11. _____	12. _____

MORE HIDDEN MEANINGS

Explain the meaning of each box.

B R A I N E D	**GROUND** FT FT FT FT FT FT	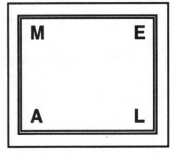
1. _____	2. *6 ft undrgrnd*	3. *square meal*

knee light	League	M a n Campus
4. _____	5. _____	6. _____

NEpainCK	**Check**	Tim
7. *pain in the neck*	8. *check up*	9. _____

Once ——— Lightly	your hat keep it	School
10. _____	11. _____	12. *highschool*

GET TO KNOW YOUR CLASSMATES

Fill each blank with the name of a classmate who fits the description. Use each person's name once. You may also include yourself.

1. Made all A's on one report card last year _____

2. Loves chocolate _____

3. Water skis _____

4. Collects stamps _____

5. Has blue eyes _____

6. Plays soccer _____

7. Was born outside the state/province _____

8. Wears contact lenses or glasses _____

9. Loves to fish _____

10. Collects football cards _____

11. Has a home computer _____

12. Is left-handed _____

13. Has visited Disneyland _____

14. Plays chess _____

15. Blue is his/her favorite color _____

16. Rides a bike to school _____

17. Has a younger sibling _____

18. Loves to read _____

19. Wears braces _____

20. Plays an instrument _____

NAMES AND NUMBERS

1. Name the two planets that have no moons._____

2. Name the three Wise Men from the biblical story. _____
    _____

3. Name the Three Stooges._____

4. Name the nine basic positions on a baseball field. _____
    _____
    _____

5. Name the original thirteen colonies in the United States._____
    _____
    _____

6. Name the four intermediate directions on a map. _____
    _____

7. Name the twelve gifts given in "The Twelve Days of Christmas." _____
    _____
    _____
    _____
    _____
    _____
    _____

8. Name the seven wonders of the ancient world._____
    _____
    _____
    _____

9. Name the seven continents. _____
    _____
    _____

10. Name the twelve provinces and territories of Canada. _____
    _____
    _____
    _____

CALCULATOR FUN

Do each math problem on your calculator. Then, turn the calculator upside-down to find an answer for each of the following clues.

	Number	Word
1. $1{,}000 - 229$ = not feeling well	_____	_____
2. $5{,}285 + 1251 + 1199$ = the opposite of buy	_____	_____
3. $70{,}000 - 34{,}999$ = not secured	_____	_____
4. $314 + 215 + 181$ = petroleum	_____	_____
5. $0.5731 + 0.2003$ = hola	_____	_____
6. $0.09 - 0.07$ = a place for animals	_____	_____
7. $188{,}308 + 188{,}308$ = to laugh in a silly way	_____	_____
8. $2{,}000 + 95 + 700 + 250$ = foot apparel	_____	_____
9. $1080 - 272$ = Robert's nickname	_____	_____
10. $0.20202 + 0.20202$ = Santa's laughter	_____	_____
11. $926 \times 2 \times 2$ = an empty space	_____	_____
12. $3544 + 3011 + 550$ = synonym for dirt	_____	_____
13. $801 - 163$ = to ask earnestly	_____	_____
14. 101×5 = a call for help	_____	_____
15. $.3 + .3$ = the opposite of stop	_____	_____

18

NUMERAL-INITIAL EQUATIONS

Each equation below contains the initials of words that will make it complete. Find the missing words. An example has been done for you.

1 = V in a S   (voice in a solo)

1. 7 = C in the R   _____

2. 13 = S on the USF   _____

3. 8 = S on an O   _____

4. 4 = Q in a G   _____

5. 12 = P and T in C   _____

6. 88 = K on a P   _____

7. 39 = B in the OT   _____

8. 144 = I in a G   _____

9. 20 = Y in a S   _____

10. 360 = D in a C   _____

11. 90 = D in a RA   _____

12. 500 = S in a R   _____

13. 1000 = M in a L   _____

14. 4 = O on E   _____

15. 16 = T in a C   _____

ADDITION AND SUBTRACTION

Place + and - signs between the digits so that both sides of each equation are equal.

1.	9	8	6	3	5	1	=	6
2.	5	3	4	4	2	9	=	17
3.	5	3	2	4	1	5	=	2
4.	3	2	1	4	1	3	=	6
5.	5	1	1	3	4	8	=	18
6.	4	9	3	7	3	1	=	19
7.	2	1	8	9	3	5	=	20
8.	8	7	1	4	4	6	=	14
9.	7	6	2	9	9	3	=	0
10.	3	5	3	9	6	5	=	15

20

THE VALUE OF WORDS

In the value box, each letter of the alphabet has been given a dollar value. To find the value of a word, add the values of all the letters. For example, the word "school" would be worth $72 (19 + 3 + 8 + 15 + 15 + 12 = 72). Write words with appropriate values in each of the boxes below.

$10 Words	$20 Words

$50 Words	$100 Words

$101–$150 Words	$151–$200 Words

VALUE BOX	
A	= $1
B	= $2
C	= $3
D	= $4
E	= $5
F	= $6
G	= $7
H	= $8
I	= $9
J	= $10
K	= $11
L	= $12
M	= $13
N	= $14
O	= $15
P	= $16
Q	= $17
R	= $18
S	= $19
T	= $20
U	= $21
V	= $22
W	= $23
X	= $24
Y	= $25
Z	= $26

GENERAL TRIVIA

1. What are the five colors on the Olympic flag? _____
    _____

2. What do we call a dead body, embalmed and preserved, as in ancient
    Egypt? _____

3. Which of Disney's seven dwarfs wears glasses? _____

4. What is the "directional" name given to left-handed people? _____

5. What do we call a picture painted on a wall? _____

6. What is the hardest mineral? _____

7. What aircraft has no engine? _____

8. What is a karat used to measure? _____

9. What does a numismatist collect? _____

10. What is the name of the month of fasting in the Muslim faith? _____
    _____

11. What is a female sheep called? _____

12. What do Christians call the Friday before Easter? _____

13. If one is superstitious, over which shoulder should one throw salt? _____

14. In the film *The Sound of Music*, how many children are there? _____

15. Who is Garfield's owner? _____

AMERICAN SOCIAL STUDIES TRIVIA

1. What does *"e pluribus unum"* mean?_____

2. How long is a senator's term of office? _____

3. Which President is shown on the five-dollar bill? _____

4. Where is the Alamo? _____

5. During what years was the Civil War fought? _____

6. Who wrote "The Pledge of Allegiance"? _____

7. The president is chief of which branch of government?_____

8. Which president's former occupation was acting? _____

9. On the flag, what does red signify?_____

10. Who became president after Dwight D. Eisenhower? _____

11. Who invented the cotton gin? _____

12. Which was the last state to join the Union? _____

13. On the Statue of Liberty, is Miss Liberty carrying the torch in her left or her right hand?_____

14. Which English explorer sailed along the West Coast in 1579? _____

    _____

15. What is the official song of the president of the United States?_____

    _____

SCIENCE TRIVIA

1. What system of the body is made of the brain, the spinal cord, and the nerves? _____

2. What comet is visible every 76 years? _____

3. In what three forms can matter exist? _____

4. What instrument is used to measure air pressure? _____

5. What do we call the dirty haze that forms when air pollution combines with moisture in the air? _____

6. What part of the body is sometimes called the "funny bone"?_____

7. What substance gives plants their green color? _____

8. What do we call the energy of motion?_____

9. What happens if the earth's crust moves suddenly along a fault? _____
   _____

10. What type of animal eats only meat? _____

11. What do all living things inhale during respiration?_____

12. Which is warmer — tepid or hot water?_____

13. What tube connects the mouth and the stomach? _____

14. What do we call pieces of stone that enter the earth's atmosphere?_____
    _____

15. What is the opening at the top of a volcano called? _____

24

MATH TRIVIA

1. Can a triangle have two right angles? _____

2. How many centimeters are there in three meters? _____

3. What does congruent mean? _____

   _____

4. Which weighs more, a pound of feathers or a pound of bricks? _____

5. What are the Roman numerals for 176? _____

6. What instrument is used to measure an angle? _____

7. In the fraction 5/9, which numeral is the numerator? _____

8. How many items are in a gross? _____

9. How many sides does a decagon have? _____

10. What is 6/8 reduced to its lowest terms?_____

11. How many zeros are in a billion? _____

12. Which angle is greater than 90 degrees — obtuse or acute? _____

    _____

13. Will perpendicular lines on the same plane ever touch?_____

14. What is the shortest distance between two points?_____

    _____

15. Is fifth an ordinal or a cardinal number?_____

ENGLISH TRIVIA

1. Who wrote *Uncle Tom's Cabin?* _____

2. What reference book contains a complete listing of synonyms and antonyms? _____

3. In grammar, what do we call the words *and, but,* and *or?* _____

4. What do we call a sentence that gives a command or makes a request?
   _____

5. What do we call the two words at the top of each dictionary page? _____
   _____

6. What three kinds of cards or computer files will you find in a card catalog?
   _____

7. Who was Tom Sawyer's best friend? _____

8. In the novel *Bunnicula,* what is the rabbit suspected of being? _____
   _____

9. What are the six parts in a business letter? _____
   _____
   _____

10. Is "Susie saw seashells at the seashore" an example of alliteration or onomatopoeia? _____

11. What do we call words that sound the same but have different meanings and spellings? _____

12. In the book *The Cricket in Times Square,* where does Chester give his concerts? _____

13. What does it mean to sign your John Hancock? _____
    _____

14. In *Charlotte's Web,* what is the last word that Charlotte writes in her web?
    _____

15. What type of books are factual? _____

TALLEST, LARGEST, OR FASTEST

What is the . . .

1. Tallest mountain?_____

2. Tallest living thing? _____

3. Tallest building?_____

4. Largest sea animal? _____

5. Largest bird? _____

6. Largest continent? _____

7. Largest island?_____

8. Largest snake? _____

9. Largest land animal? _____

10. Fastest sea animal? _____

11. Fastest land animal?_____

12. Fastest flying animal? _____

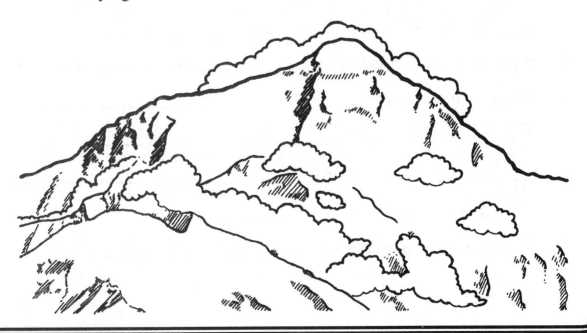

HOW MANY?

Answer each question with a number. How many . . .

1. Eyes did Cyclops have?_____

2. Planets in our solar system have no moons?_____

3. Sides does a pentagon have? _____

4. Teeth does an adult have? _____

5. Degrees are in a right angle?_____

6. Centimeters are in a meter? _____

7. Faces are carved on Mt. Rushmore? _____

8. Musical instruments are played in an *a cappella* performance?_____

9. Stories are in the Sears Tower? _____

10. Degrees are in a circle? _____

11. Bones are in the body? _____

12. Items are in a gross? _____

13. Lines of verse in a sonnet? _____

14. Cards are in a deck?_____

15. Squares are on a checkerboard? _____

16. Years are in a century?_____

17. Days are in a leap year?_____

18. Sheets of paper are in a ream?_____

19. Keys are on a piano? _____

20. People are on a football team? _____

WHICH IS IT?

Circle the word or number on the right that correctly corresponds to the word or words on the left.

1.	Octagon	4 sides	6 sides	8 sides
2.	People aboard the *Mayflower*	75	102	132
3.	State	Oklahoma	Canada	Springfield
4.	Thomas Jefferson	16th president	3rd president	40th president
5.	Painter	Picasso	Bach	Shakespeare
6.	Province	Alaska	Montreal	Quebec
7.	Baker's dozen	12	13	15
8.	Decagon	10 sides	12 sides	15 sides
9.	Year	12 months	50 weeks	360 days
10.	Percussion instrument	trombone	violin	tambourine
11.	Cloud formation	omnibus	cumulus	calculus
12.	Capital of California	Sacramento	Los Angeles	Hollywood
13.	Day	12 hours	24 hours	60 minutes
14.	Century	10 years	20 years	100 years
15.	Muscles in the human body	over 200	over 350	over 600
16.	Mother's Day	February	May	June

RHYMING WORD PAIRS

Find an adjective that rhymes with a noun so that together the two words have about the same meaning as the phrase that is given. An example has been done for you.

A soaked dog = soggy doggy

1. A friend who does not arrive on time _____

2. An overweight rodent _____

3. A naughty boy _____

4. A crude guy _____

5. A beetle's cup _____

6. A lengthy tune _____

7. An overweight feline _____

8. Twice as much bother _____

9. A large hog _____

10. A girl from Switzerland_____

11. A skinny horse_____

12. A 100-watt bulb_____

13. A comical rabbit _____

14. A happy boy_____

15. A loafing flower_____

16. An unhappy father _____

17. A home for a rodent_____

18. Without money_____

19. An irritated employer_____

20. Fake coins _____

HYPHENS

Rewrite the words below, inserting hyphens or spaces if and where they are needed.

1. selfservice   _____

2. coauthor   _____

3. ups and downs   _____

4. absentminded   _____

5. lightfooted   _____

6. weatherbureau   _____

7. nonexistent   _____

8. threefifths   _____

9. rollerskates   _____

10. warmblooded   _____

11. icecream   _____

12. allready   _____

13. adlib   _____

14. jacko'lantern   _____

15. eightyfive   _____

16. uptodate   _____

17. autobiography   _____

18. drivein   _____

WHICH WORD?

Words that sound or look alike often have meanings that are not alike at all. Decide which of the two word choices on the right is the correct one to correspond with the word or phrase on the left, and then circle it.

1. Dry land   desert/dessert

2. Reno, Nevada   capital/capitol

3. Complete   through/thorough

4. In any case   any way/anyway

5. A result   affect/effect

6. To hint or suggest   imply/infer

7. Second in a series of two   later/latter

8. A heavenly body   angel/angle

9. Unlawful   illicit/elicit

10. To prove something is false   disapprove/disprove

11. Writing paper   stationary/stationery

12. To take that which is offered   accept/except

13. To go forward   precede/proceed

14. A part of speech   preposition/proposition

15. To stop   quit/quite

PALINDROMES

Palindromes are words, phrases, sentences, or numbers that read the same forward and backward. Write a palindrome that relates to each word or phrase below. An example has been done for you.

Trick or joke = gag

1. Midday _____
2. Past tense of the verb do _____
3. A female sheep _____
4. Robert's nickname _____
5. A small child _____
6. A little chick's noise _____
7. An organ of the body used for sight _____
8. A father's nickname _____
9. Something that fails to work _____
10. The sound of a horn _____
11. Something a baby wears _____
12. Songs sung alone _____
13. A mother's nickname _____
14. An Eskimo canoe _____
15. Even, flat _____
16. Soda _____
17. A woman's name _____
18. A small dog _____
19. A brave or skillful act _____
20. Relating to government or citizenship _____

ACRONYMS

Acronyms are words formed from the initial letters of the words for which they stand. An example is VIP, which means "very important person." What do the following acronyms mean?

1. AWOL _____

2. RSVP _____

3. MADD _____

4. POW _____

5. RV _____

6. UNICEF _____

7. TLC _____

8. GI _____

9. SWAT _____

10. COD _____

11. BLT _____

12. IQ _____

13. RIP _____

14. ASAP _____

15. TGIF _____

CLIPPED WORDS

The following words are written in their shortened form. Write the long form of these words in the blanks to their right.

1. phone   _____

2. champ   _____

3. gas   _____

4. vet   _____

5. pop   _____

6. bike   _____

7. plane   _____

8. tux   _____

9. math   _____

10. ref   _____

11. auto   _____

12. fridge _____

13. sub   _____

14. prom   _____

15. gym   _____

16. taxi   _____

17. burger _____

18. specs   _____

19. limo   _____

20. exam   _____

WORD CHAIN

Each phrase below is a clue to a word. However, each word is part of a chain whereby the last two letters of one word in the chain begin the next word. Continue throughout the chain in this way. The first two have been done for you.

1. The capital of Idaho   Boi<u>se</u>

2. A few   <u>se</u>veral

3. Very nearly   _____

4. Unyielding, firm   _____

5. A powerful explosive   _____

6. A dark grayish blue   _____

7. A kind of llama   _____

8. A nut   _____

9. A female sheep   _____

10. The fourth day of the week   _____

11. Yes   _____

12. A primary color   _____

13. A young owl   _____

14. And so forth   _____

15. A vegetable that grows underground   _____

16. A hut   _____

17. A small child   _____

18. A musical instrument   _____

19. For protection against the rain   _____

20. A weapon   _____

COMPETITIVE WORD CHAIN

Two or more players can begin this game at the same time. The object is to fill in all the blanks with a 3-, 4-, or 5-letter word, depending on the number of blanks given. Each word must begin with the last letter of the preceding word. The first word may start with any letter. (Words may not be repeated.) The first player to fill in all the blanks wins.

1. __ __ __
2. __ __ __ __
3. __ __ __ __ __
4. __ __ __ __
5. __ __ __
6. __ __ __ __
7. __ __ __ __ __
8. __ __ __
9. __ __ __
10. __ __ __ __
11. __ __ __ __ __
12. __ __ __ __
13. __ __ __
14. __ __ __ __
15. __ __ __ __ __
16. __ __ __
17. __ __ __
18. __ __ __ __
19. __ __ __ __
20. __ __ __

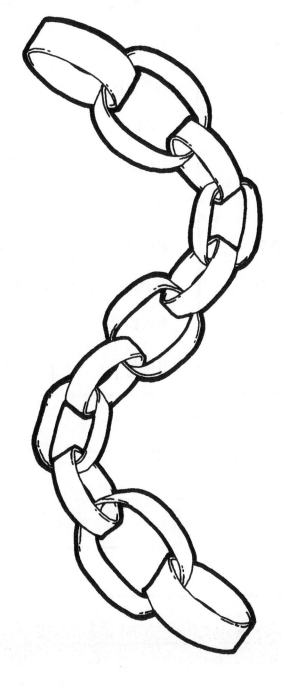

COMPOUND WORDS

Choose a word from column A or B and combine it with a word from column C or D to make a compound word. Some words will go together in more than one combination, but there is only one combination that uses all of the words.

Col. A	Col. B	Col. C	Col. D
any-	hand-	-pole	-side
base-	down-	-come	-ball
under-	paint-	-where	-port
in-	flag-	-box	-father
camp-	light-	-brush	-town
rail-	eye-	-ground	-line
grand-	mail-	-road	-house
north-	over-	-shake	-lid
quarter-	text-	-back	-book
sea-	junk-	-east	-yard

_____   _____   _____   _____

_____   _____   _____   _____

_____   _____   _____   _____

_____   _____   _____   _____

_____   _____   _____   _____

38

PUTTING THE PIECES TOGETHER

Choose one syllable each from columns A, B, and C to form three-syllable words. Write the new words in column D. Use each syllable only once. One has been done for you.

Column A	Cloumn B	Column C	Column D
as	ta	cine	aspirin
guar	di	tion	
med	pi	tone	
set	por	er	
im	fer	sine	
con	ou	tant	
o	an	mal	
ear	di	est	
lim	for	um	
dif	li	mins	
brav	tle	ent	
ra	on	tee	
pris	i	ment	
in	ver	y	
vi	er	rin	

WORD WINDERS

Use the clues to help you fill in the blanks and circles. Only the circled letters change from one word to the next. The first two have been done for you. (Note: When a word has fewer spaces than the word above it, simply drop the letter above the empty space.)

1. Pointed   <u>s h a r p</u>

2. A fish that can be dangerous   <u>s h a r k</u>

3. To use together

4. To be concerned

5. A navigator's map

6. To delight

7. Not soft

8. Synonym for rabbit

9. Money paid to ride a bus

10. Land used to raise crops

11. A signal used to give warning

12. A small songbird

13. The sound a dog makes

14. Without light

15. To have sufficient courage

16. A fruit

17. After the usual time

18. A bowling alley

19. A walking stick

20. A wafer for holding ice cream

21. Finished

LETTER ANSWERS

Use one, two, or three letters of the alphabet to "spell" a word corresponding to each of the following clues. The first one has been done for you.

1. Used in a pool game   <u>   Q   </u>

2. Happiness   _____

3. A foe   _____

4. Jealousy   _____

5. An insect   _____

6. A verb of debt   _____

7. A written composition   _____

8. Not difficult   _____

9. A boy's name   _____

10. To say good-bye   _____

11. The number after 79   _____

12. A body of water   _____

13. An exclamation   _____

14. To be good at something   _____

15. To rot   _____

ONE WORD PLUS ANOTHER

Add one word to another word to make a third word. The first one has been done for you.

1. A water barrier plus a writing utensil equals a verb that means "to make slightly wet."

   dam + pen = dampen

2. A large body of water plus a male child make a period of time.

   _____ + _____ = _____

3. A lightweight bed of canvas plus 2,000 pounds make a type of fabric.

   _____ + _____ = _____

4. A vegetable plus an edible kernel make a seed that ripens underground and is usually roasted before being eaten.

   _____ + _____ = _____

5. The nearest star plus the antonym of *wet* make an adjective meaning "various" or "several."

   _____ + _____ = _____

6. A male offspring plus something used to catch fish make a form of poetry.

   _____ + _____ = _____

7. The antonym of *on* plus frozen water make a place for business.

   _____ + _____ = _____

8. A rodent plus a shade of brown make a plant used to make furniture.

   _____ + _____ = _____

9. Male adults plus the highest playing card make a threat.

   _____ + _____ = _____

10. A man's name plus a male child make the name of a former U.S. president.

    _____ + _____ = _____

42

COLORFUL WORDS

Answer each clue with a word or phrase that has the name of a color in it. There may be more than one answer.

1. A bridge in California   _____

2. A chocolate cookie-like cake   _____

3. A flower   _____

4. A bird   _____

5. A person without training or experience   _____

6. A fruit   _____

7. A contagious disease   _____

8. A wasp   _____

9. A bus line   _____

10. A piece of slate on which to write with chalk   _____

11. An automobile tire   _____

12. Beef, lamb, and veal   _____

13. A medal   _____

14. A famous pirate   _____

CORN-FED WORDS

Each phrase below is a clue for a word or phrase that contains the letters CORN.

1. A horn of plenty_____

2. Something of fundamental importance _____

3. Where two streets meet _____

4. A type of sandwich meat_____

5. The center part of an ear of corn _____

6. A building for storing corn _____

7. A position in football_____

8. A product used in cooking and salads_____

9. An instrument that looks like a trumpet _____

10. The kind of joke that makes people groan _____

11. The outer covering of the eyeball _____

12. A way to save money, time, or effort (two words) _____

13. A thickening agent in gravy_____

14. An ornamental molding along the top of a wall _____

15. A breakfast cereal _____

FAR OUT

Each phrase below is a clue for a word or phrase that contains the letters FAR.

1. The price of a bus ride _____

2. A minor league club _____

3. A paid worker on a farm _____

4. A litter of pigs _____

5. At a greater distance _____

6. One who raises crops _____

7. Remote _____

8. Good-by _____

9. A former British coin of little value _____

10. Not ordinarily pertinent _____

11. A region of Asia _____

12. Up to this point all is well _____

13. Humor based on ridiculous happenings _____

14. To overstep reasonable limits _____

15. Having widespread influence _____

PET PEEVES

Each phrase below is a clue for a word or phrase that contains the letters PET.

1. A man's name _____

2. Turned to stone _____

3. Part of a flower _____

4. A floor covering _____

5. Occurring again and again_____

6. A figure controlled by the movement of strings or hands _____

7. Small, tiny _____

8. A flower_____

9. An underskirt_____

10. Liquid used to make gasoline _____

11. A naval officer_____

12. Small amounts of money for incidental expenses_____

13. A formal request, often signed by a large number of people _____

14. A shallow glass container used to prepare cultures in science labs _____

_____

15. A small cake with fancy frosting _____

46

THIS "ORE" THAT

Each phrase below is a clue for a word or phrase that contains the letters ORE.

1. Land next to a body of water _____

2. An ancestor _____

3. In a plentiful amount _____

4. A state in the U.S. _____

5. Took an oath _____

6. The finger next to the thumb _____

7. A routine task _____

8. To breathe loudly during sleep _____

9. A seasoning used in cooking _____

10. To love or worship _____

11. To predict the weather _____

12. Woods _____

13. Opposite of less _____

14. Animals that eat only meat _____

15. To choose not to pay attention _____

"THE" WORDS

Each phrase below is a clue for a word or phrase that contains the letters THE.

1. Used to keep liquids warm or cold _____

2. Near that place or time _____

3. The study of numbers _____

4. Instrument used to measure temperature_____

5. Melody used to identify a certain show _____

6. To bring together _____

7. The act of stealing _____

8. A dictionary of synonyms and antonyms _____

9. An essay submitted by a candidate for a university degree _____

10. To wash; to immerse in liquid_____

11. An explanation; an opinion _____

12. At that time _____

13. A black leopard _____

14. The atmospheric conditions of a place _____

15. A place where movies are shown _____

MAN HUNT

Each phrase below is a clue for a word or phrase that contains the letters MAN.

1. A large insect _____

2. A tropical fruit _____

3. A shelf above a fireplace _____

4. A feeding trough for cattle _____

5. A province in Canada _____

6. To make by hand or by machine _____

7. Numerous _____

8. A small orange _____

9. A stringed musical instrument _____

10. Treatment for fingernails _____

11. An opening to a sewer _____

12. Person in charge _____

13. A large house _____

14. To treat roughly _____

15. A model for displaying clothes _____

DECODING I

Each group of letters below is a list of related names written in code. Each group has its own code. Brainstorm some names to fit each category. Then, try to match one of the names to the code. Once you have identified a name, use the known letters to decode the other names.

Famous Women

1. FTNGK A PCOQ   _____

2. RTKTH QTKKTG   _____

3. TKTNHJG GJJATITKW   _____

4. OKNGN PNGWJH   _____

5. LNHT NEENZA   _____

6. NZTKSN TNGRNGW   _____

7. KNCGN SHDNKKA USKETG   _____

8. ACANH P NHWRJHM   _____

9. RNGGSTW WCPZNH   _____

10. ANKKM GSET   _____

Deserts

1. NLSKM FLKM   _____

2. HGECST   _____

3. TCNGST   _____

4. JQSLV HSTTQI   _____

5. BQRSE   _____

6. HSVSFS   _____

7. RFQSL HSBJG   _____

8. DLPSEQ   _____

9. HLBLFSB   _____

10. RLKC   _____

50

DECODING II

Each group of letters below is a list of related names written in code. Each group has its own code. Brainstorm some names to fit each category. Then, try to match one of the names to the code. Once you have identified a name, use the known letters to decode the other names.

U.S. Landmarks

1. KCBJF GLWJF VRSRJG _____

2. TDLJU NLJPCJ _____

3. ARLDS VLDOCD _____

4. KCBJF DBGVKCDR _____

5. KCBJF KNEWJSRP _____

6. TLFRHLP LDNV _____

7. HVWFR VCBGR _____

8. ASPKCBFV DCNE _____

9. GFLFBR CQ SWORDFP _____

10. CSU QLWFVQBS _____

Explorers

1. LDCP _____

2. LESLIE _____

3. OELIM _____

4. TIBOK PK SKIB _____

5. ESKGEBPKC MQK NCKEM _____

6. FKUTROOA _____

7. OISRVLRU _____

8. SKZAU EBP OSECX _____

9. OICIBEPI _____

10. OECMAKC _____

DECODING III

Each group of letters below is a list of related words or names written in code. Each group has its own code. Brainstorm some words/names to fit each category. Then, try to match one of them to the code. Once you have identified a word/name, use the known letters to decode the other ones in the list.

Clouds

1. FENREWTBHBZBF _____
2. TBHBZWCGHABF _____
3. RZEWTBHBZBF _____
4. CGHAWFENREBF _____
5. FENREBF _____
6. TGNNWFENREBF _____
7. TBHBZBF _____
8. TGNNBF _____
9. RZEWFENREBF _____

North American Nations

1. GNLNENB _____
2. ANPNON _____
3. KDNQHENJN _____
4. EHICAM _____
5. HJ BNJRNOMT _____
6. DPCQHO BQNQHB _____
7. AMBQN TCAN _____
8. SNENCAN _____
9. ADGN _____

EDUCATION

List all the words you can make from the letters in "education." All the words in your list must have at least three letters, and each letter can be used only once in each word.

I AM TERRIFIC

List all the words you can make from the letters in "I am terrific." All the words in your list must have at least three letters, and each letter can be used only once in each word for each time it appears in the original phrase.

—————————— —————————— ——————————

—————————— —————————— ——————————

—————————— —————————— ——————————

—————————— —————————— ——————————

—————————— —————————— ——————————

—————————— —————————— ——————————

—————————— —————————— ——————————

—————————— —————————— ——————————

—————————— —————————— ——————————

—————————— —————————— ——————————

—————————— —————————— ——————————

—————————— —————————— ——————————

—————————— —————————— ——————————

—————————— —————————— ——————————

—————————— —————————— ——————————

—————————— —————————— ——————————

—————————— —————————— ——————————

WHERE IN THE UNITED STATES?

Find the letters in the words "United States" to write the answers to the following clues.

1. To make fun of in a playful or unkind way _____

2. To rise to one's feet _____

3. A female relative _____

4. To be in want of _____

5. To be present at _____

6. Five plus five _____

7. An exam _____

8. Earth's source of energy _____

9. Past tense of eat _____

10. To sample a food _____

11. Tiny grains on the beach _____

12. A body of water _____

13. To join together _____

14. A lodging for campers _____

15. The home of a lion _____

16. A large sea fish _____

17. When the sun goes down _____

18. A place to sit _____

19. A melody _____

20. To finish _____

PROVERBS

Proverbs are old, familiar sayings that often give advice for daily living. Complete each of the following proverbs and explain what it means.

1. Haste makes . . . _____

2. A penny saved . . . _____

   _____

3. The early bird . . . _____

   _____

4. When the cat's away, . . . _____

5. Don't count your chickens . . . _____

   _____

6. Never put off until tomorrow . . . _____

   _____

7. Don't look a gift horse . . . _____

   _____

8. Look before . . . _____

   _____

9. Birds of a feather . . . _____

   _____

10. Early to bed and early to rise . . . _____

   _____

ANOTHER PUZZLING PROVERB

Fill in the answers to the following clues. Then, transfer the letters to the corresponding numbered blanks to reveal a famous proverb.

1. Food prepared scrambled or fried
$$\overline{}_{31} \quad \overline{}_{20} \quad \overline{}_{4} \quad \overline{}_{8}$$

2. To keep out of sight
$$\overline{}_{2} \quad \overline{}_{38} \quad \overline{}_{39} \quad \overline{}_{23}$$

3. Plural of *this*
$$\overline{}_{29} \quad \overline{}_{34} \quad \overline{}_{22} \quad \overline{}_{7} \quad \overline{}_{40}$$

4. Solitary
$$\overline{}_{10} \quad \overline{}_{17} \quad \overline{}_{28} \quad \overline{}_{25}$$

5. Feeling regret
$$\overline{}_{19} \quad \overline{}_{32} \quad \overline{}_{36} \quad \overline{}_{5} \quad \overline{}_{13}$$

6. Australian tree-climbing animal
$$\overline{}_{18} \quad \overline{}_{27} \quad \overline{}_{6} \quad \overline{}_{15} \quad \overline{}_{12}$$

7. By preference
$$\overline{}_{21} \quad \overline{}_{9} \quad \overline{}_{1} \quad \overline{}_{30} \quad \overline{}_{35} \quad \overline{}_{26}$$

8. Not old
$$\overline{}_{24} \quad \overline{}_{3} \quad \overline{}_{11}$$

9. To throw without force
$$\overline{}_{33} \quad \overline{}_{16} \quad \overline{}_{14} \quad \overline{}_{37}$$

$$\overline{}_{1} \quad \overline{}_{2} \quad \overline{}_{3} \qquad \overline{}_{4} \quad \overline{}_{5} \quad \overline{}_{6} \quad \overline{}_{7} \quad \overline{}_{8} \qquad \overline{}_{38} \quad \overline{}_{19}$$

$$\overline{}_{9} \quad \overline{}_{10} \quad \overline{}_{11} \quad \overline{}_{12} \quad \overline{}_{13} \quad \overline{}_{14}$$

$$\overline{}_{20} \quad \overline{}_{21} \quad \overline{}_{22} \quad \overline{}_{23} \quad \overline{}_{24} \quad \overline{}_{25} \quad \overline{}_{26} \qquad \overline{}_{27} \quad \overline{}_{28}$$

$$\overline{}_{29} \quad \overline{}_{30} \quad \overline{}_{31} \qquad \overline{}_{32} \quad \overline{}_{33} \quad \overline{}_{34} \quad \overline{}_{35} \quad \overline{}_{36} \qquad \overline{}_{37} \quad \overline{}_{38} \quad \overline{}_{39} \quad \overline{}_{40}$$

CODED MESSAGE

Circle the correct letter for each problem below. Then, take the circled letter and put it in the corresponding blank in order to reveal a famous saying.

$$\overline{7}\ \overline{2}\ \overline{6}\qquad \overline{8}\ \overline{5}\ \overline{3}\qquad \overline{11}\ \overline{1}\qquad \overline{7}\ \overline{2}\ \overline{6}$$

$$\overline{9}\ \overline{4}\ \overline{11}\ \overline{3}\ \overline{10}\qquad \overline{7}\ \overline{2}\ \overline{6}\qquad \overline{8}\ \overline{5}\ \overline{3}$$

1. If man walked on the moon in 1492, circle S. If not, circle F.

2. If a prairie dog is a dog, circle K. It it is a rodent, circle O.

3. If your father's sister is your aunt, circle N. If not, circle A.

4. If 6 x 9 = 55, circle M. If not, circle H.

5. If antonyms are words that mean the opposite of one another, circle A. If not, circle L.

6. If Brazil is a country in Europe, circle K. If not, circle U.

7. If the capital of Illinois is Springfield, circle Y. If not circle, U.

8. If the trumpet is a woodwind instrument, circle Z. If not, circle C.

9. If Charles Dickens wrote *David Copperfield*, circle T. If not, circle W.

10. If a telescope is used to view things far away, circle K. If not, circle M.

11. If the Statue of Liberty is located in Washington, D.C., circle E. It not, circle I.

DOUBLE LETTERS

Use the following clues to find words that contain consecutive double letters.

1. A favorable set of circumstances_____

2. A winged insect, usually brightly colored_____

3. A storm with wind and snow_____

4. Mental ability_____

5. Not guilty_____

6. To move with short, quick movements; squirm _____

7. A space with nothing in it, not even air _____

8. Earth's natural satellite _____

9. To draw absent-mindedly _____

10. One who expects bad things to happen_____

11. To get or use temporarily_____

12. An animal with a long neck_____ _____

13. A flock of geese_____

14. A sport in which touchdowns are scored _____

15. A pirate _____

16. Part of a word pronounced as a unit _____

17. Grief, sadness_____

18. A sale of goods to raise funds, especially for charity _____

19. To make something seem larger or better than it is _____

20. A long, tapering flag _____

BEGIN AND END

Each phrase below is a clue for an answer that begins and ends with the same letter.

1. A continent at the south pole _____

2. Payment to stockholders _____

3. A word used by magicians _____

4. Physical exertion done for fitness _____

5. One television show in a series _____

6. One who reviews and gives judgements _____

7. A brief advertisement _____

8. A place for performers _____

9. An amount over and above what is needed _____

10. A great work of art or literature _____

11. A ray of moonlight _____

12. An edible seed of a bean plant _____

13. Accepting of others _____

14. Handwriting skill _____

15. Blue-green _____

16. An official list of names _____

17. One thousand years _____

A TO B

Write a word that begins with "A" and ends with "B". Continue through the alphabet, finishing with a word that begins with "Z" and ends with "A".

A _____ B

B _____ C

C _____ D

D _____ E

E _____ F

F _____ G

G _____ H

H _____ I

I _____ J

J _____ K

K _____ L

L _____ M

M _____ N

N _____ O

O _____ P

P _____ Q

Q _____ R

R _____ S

S _____ T

T _____ U

U _____ V

V _____ W

W _____ X

X _____ Y

Y _____ Z

Z _____ A

A TO A TO Z TO Z

Brainstorm words that begin and end with the same letter. You may not find any words for some letters.

A _____

B _____

C _____

D _____

E _____

F _____

G _____

H _____

I _____

J _____

K _____

L _____

M _____

N _____

O _____

P _____

Q _____

R _____

S _____

T _____

U _____

V _____

W _____

X _____

Y _____

Z _____

INVENTIONS

Inventions are products that people have created which contribute to our lives. Brainstorm some inventions that begin with each letter of the alphabet.

A _____
B _____
C _____
D _____
E _____
F _____
G _____
H _____
I _____
J _____
K _____
L _____
M _____
N _____
O _____
P _____
Q _____
R _____
S _____
T _____
U _____
V _____
W _____
X _____
Y _____
Z _____

FROM A TO Z

Find a word that begins with A and ends with Z, begins with B and ends with Y, and so on. You may not find a word for every pair.

A _____ Z   N_____ M

B _____ Y   O _____ L

C _____ X   P _____ K

D_____ W   Q _____ J

E _____ V   R _____ I

F _____ U   S _____ H

G _____ T   T _____ G

H _____ S   U _____ F

I _____ R   V _____ E

J _____ Q   W_____ D

K _____ P   X _____ C

L _____ O   Y _____ B

M_____ N   Z _____ A

64

TWO OF A KIND

Make a list of words that contain two of each letter: two A's, two B's, two C's, and so forth. The letters do not need to be next to one another.

A _____

B _____

C _____

D _____

E _____

F _____

G _____

H _____

I _____

J _____

K _____

L _____

M _____

N _____

O _____

P _____

Q _____

R _____

S _____

T _____

U _____

V _____

W _____

X _____

Y _____

Z _____

ALL FIVE VOWELS

Make a list of words that have all five vowels within them.

ANALOGIES

Analogies are comparisons. Complete each analogy below. An example has been done for you.

Tall is to short as wide is to narrow.

1. _____ is to aunt as nephew is to uncle.

2. Eat is to_____ as sleep is to tired.

3. Zoo is to animals as _____ is to books.

4. Eye is to sight as ear is to_____.

5. November is to Thanksgiving as_____ is to Christmas.

6. Small is to _____as little is to big.

7. _____ is to waist as bracelet is to wrist.

8. Grape is to _____ as cherry is to tree.

9. Blue is to sky as _____ is to grass.

10. Shoe is to foot as hat is to _____.

11. Cub is to lion as _____ is to cow.

12. Dusk is to _____ as night is to day.

13. _____ is to read as radio is to listen.

14. Ship is to _____ as airplane is to pilot.

15. Floor is to bottom as_____ is to top.

16. Gate is to yard as door is to _____.

17. Boy is to man as _____ is to woman.

18. Window is to_____ as floor is to rug.

19. _____ is to nest as bee is to hive.

20. Boat is to _____ as car is to road.

SIMILES

Similes are figures of speech that compare two things by using the words "like" or "as." An example is "as sharp as a tack." Complete the following common similes. Then, write five additional similes of your own.

1. As fresh as _____

2. As smooth as _____

3. As mad as _____

4. As clean as _____

5. As strong as _____

6. As proud as _____

7. As easy as _____

8. As happy as _____

9. As neat as _____

10. As white as _____

11. As quick as _____

12. As red as _____

13. As pale as _____

14. As slippery as _____

15. As slow as _____

16. _____

17. _____

18. _____

19. _____

20. _____

IDIOMS

Idioms are expressions whose meanings are different from the literal ones. Explain what the idioms below actually mean.

1. If Grandpa loves to spin a yarn, he _____
_____

2. "When Dad finally put his foot down, my sister started to do better in school," said Andrew. What Andrew meant was _____
_____

3. When Ryan asked Chelsea, "Are you getting cold feet?" he was actually asking _____
_____

4. When Jessica said, "That movie took my breath away," she meant _____
_____
_____

5. Morgan stood and said, "I guess I'll hit the road now." What Morgan meant was _____
_____

6. When Phil says that he was in the dark about what was going on, he meant
_____

7. "Hold your horses young man," remarked the police officer. The police officer meant _____
_____

8. When Nicole said that she slept like a log last night, she meant _____
_____
_____

9. When Tabitha said that she was a bit under the weather last weekend, she meant _____
_____

10. "I'll be in the doghouse for sure," exclaimed Miguel. What Miguel really meant was _____
_____

SYNONYMS, ANTONYMS, HOMOPHONES

Identify each pair of words as synonyms (S), antonyms (A), or homophones (H).

1. clause-claws _____

2. problem-solution _____

3. ally-friend _____

4. following-preceding _____

5. attempt-endeavor _____

6. vast-minute _____

7. accept-except _____

8. sufficient-enough _____

9. foe-opposition _____

10. beautiful-gorgeous _____

11. manner-manor _____

12. crave-desire _____

13. individual-group _____

14. troublesome-difficult _____

15. stationery-stationary _____

16. maximum-minimum _____

17. frequently-repeatedly _____

18. join-separate _____

19. unique-different _____

20. him-hymn _____

DO YOU KNOW NOSE EXPRESSIONS?

Write the meanings of these "nose" expressions on the blanks below.

1. To cut off one's nose to spite one's face _____
   _____

2. To turn up one's nose _____
   _____

3. To win by a nose _____
   _____

4. To put someone's nose out of joint _____
   _____

5. To stick one's nose in _____
   _____

6. To follow one's nose _____
   _____

7. To pay through the nose _____
   _____

8. Under one's nose _____
   _____

9. To look down one's nose _____
   _____

10. On the nose _____
    _____

INEDIBLE FOOD

The following expressions refer to food, but they do not have anything to do with eating. Explain what the following expressions mean.

1. To take it with a grain of salt _____

2. Full of beans _____

3. To bring home the bacon _____

4. The apple of one's eye _____

5. To cook up _____

6. Egg on one's face _____

7. Cool as a cucumber _____

8. A hot dog _____

9. To talk turkey _____

10. To ham it up _____

11. A rotten egg _____

12. High on the hog _____

13. Full of baloney _____

14. Meat and potatoes _____

15. To cook one's own goose _____

BODY LANGUAGE

Fill in the blanks with the names of the body part normally used in the phrases below.

1. He got his_____ in the door.

2. Her _____ is to the wall.

3. He is so thin that he's nothing but _____ and _____.

4. Keep a stiff upper_____.

5. The captain called, "All _____ on deck."

6. She made it by the skin of her _____.

7. I wanted him to get to the_____ of the matter.

8. They do not see _____ to _____.

9. My grandparents have an old-fashioned pot-_____ stove.

10. Do not stick your _____ out unless it is worth it to you.

11. She knew that it went in one _____ and out the other.

12. To tell time, he used his new_____ watch.

13. He is really out on a_____.

14. When he told me, he had a lump in his _____.

15. She is_____ and _____ above the rest.

ANIMAL FAMILIES AND GROUPS

Fill in the blanks in the chart.

Animal	Male	Female	Young	Group
fox	dog	_____	_____	skulk
_____	rooster	hen	_____	_____
lion	_____	lioness	_____	pride
cattle	bull	_____	calf	_____
whale	_____	cow	calf	_____
seal	bull	_____	pup	_____
ostrich	cock	hen	_____	flock
sheep	_____	ewe	_____	flock
goose	gander	_____	gosling	gaggle
kangaroo	_____	doe	_____	_____
hog	_____	sow	_____	herd
_____	billy	nanny	kid	herd

ANSWER KEY

Page 3
1. Lois Lane
2. Cleopatra
3. Harriet
4. Gretel
5. Wilbur
6. Hardy
7. Maid Marian
8. Clark
9. Delilah
10. Juliet
11. Dagwood
12. Costello
13. Hobbes
14. Tweety
15. Shirley

Page 4
1. found
2. forth
3. bad
4. wide (near)
5. blue (white)
6. potatoes
7. eggs
8. nails
9. pains
10. match
11. joy
12. proper
13. foot
14. cheese
15. butter (water)
16. onions
17. go
18. needles
19. go
20. wrong
21. right
22. dance
23. saucer
24. down (away)
25. sound
26. bolts
27. thin
28. write
29. beans
30. fork
31. no
32. water
33. learn (let live)
34. go (think)
35. pepper
36. stones
37. turn
38. low (dry)
39. then (later)
40. nail

Page 5
Answers will vary.

Page 6
1. cry; expressions of humor
2. sun; signs of bad weather
3. tomato; flowers
4. math; reference books
5. nephew; female relatives
6. gosling; hog family
7. blood; organs in the body
8. Oklahoma; states bordering the Pacific Ocean
9. chicken; animals with 4 legs
10. hamburgers; condiments
11. Bears; baseball teams
12. eraser; writing tools
13. margarine; grain products
14. green; primary colors
15. watermelon; citrus fruits

Page 7
1. Tom
2. David
3. Jordi
4. Greg
5. Jeff
6. Andrew
7. Luis
8. Phil
9. Carlos

Page 8
Becky: elephants and ice cream
Alexis: monkeys and snowcone
Lindsey: lions and popcorn
Brooke: horses and taffy

Page 9
Ms. Snow: Illinois, math, and Chinese
Mr. Hunter: Nevada, science, and Mexican
Mr. Wong: Wisconsin, English, and Italian
Mrs. Jackson: California, geography, American

Page 10
David: jogging for 15 minutes
Tom: bicycling for 45 minutes
Rick: golfing for 30 minutes
Roger: swimming for 60 minutes

Page 11

Page 12

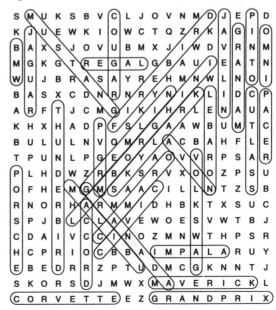

ANSWER KEY *(cont.)*

Page 13

Answers will vary.

Page 14

1. face to face
2. man overboard
3. split level
4. long underwear
5. deer crossing
6. head over heels
7. business before pleasure
8. order in the court
9. uptown
10. banana split
11. three degrees below zero
12. Minnesota

Page 15

1. scatterbrained
2. six feet below the ground
3. a square meal
4. neon light
5. little league
6. big man on campus
7. pain in the neck
8. check up
9. Tiny Tim
10. once over lightly
11. keep it under your hat
12. high school

Page 16

Answers will vary.

Page 17

1. Mercury and Venus
2. Casper, Melchior, and Balthasar
3. Larry, Mo, and Curly (or Curly Jo)
4. pitcher, catcher, first base, second base, third base, right field, left field, center field, short stop
5. Massachusetts, Connecticut, Rhode Island, New Hampshire, New York, New Jersey, Pennsylvania, Delaware, Maryland, Virginia, North Carolina, South Carolina, and Georgia
6. northeast, southeast, northwest, and southwest
7. a partridge in a pear tree, two turtle doves, three French hens, four colly birds, five golden rings, six geese a-laying, seven swans a-swimming, eight maids a-milking, nine drummers drumming, ten pipers piping, eleven ladies dancing, and twelve lords a-leaping
8. pyramids, hanging gardens of Babylon, statue of Zeus, temple of Diana at Ephesus, mausoleum at Halicarnassus, colossus at Rhodes, and the lighthouse at Pharos
9. North America, South America, Europe, Asia, Antarctica, Africa, and Australia

10. Alberta, British Columbia, Manitoba, New Brunswick, Newfoundland, Northwest Territories, Nova Scotia, Ontario, Prince Edward Island, Quebec, Saskatchewan, and Yukon Territory

Page 18

1. 771; ill
2. 7735; sell
3. 35001; loose
4. 710; oil
5. 0.7734; hello
6. 0.02; zoo
7. 376616; giggle
8. 3045; shoe
9. 808; Bob
10. 0.40404; hohoho
11. 3704; hole
12. 7105; soil
13. 638; beg
14. 505; SOS
15. .09; go

Page 19

1. colors in the rainbow
2. stripes on the U.S. flag
3. sides on an octagon
4. quarts in a gallon
5. provinces and territories in Canada
6. keys on a piano
7. books in the Old Testament
8. items in a gross
9. years in a score
10. degrees in a circle
11. degrees in a right angle
12. sheets in a ream
13. milliliters in a liter
14. oceans on Earth
15. tablespoons in a cup

Page 20

1. - + + - +
2. - + + - +
3. + + - + - or - + + - -
4. + - + + -
5. - - + + +
6. + - + + -
7. - + + - +
8. + + - - + or - - + + +
9. - + + - -
10. + - + + -

Page 21

Answers will vary.

Page 22

1. black, red, yellow, blue, and green
2. a mummy
3. Doc
4. southpaws
5. a mural
6. a diamond
7. a glider
8. gold
9. coins

10. Ramadan
11. a ewe
12. Good Friday
13. the left shoulder
14. seven
15. Jon Arbukle

Page 23

1. "Out of many, one"
2. six years
3. Abraham Lincoln
4. San Antonio, Texas
5. 1861–1865
6. Francis Bellamy
7. the executive branch
8. Ronald Reagan
9. courage
10. John F. Kennedy
11. Eli Whitney
12. Hawaii
13. her right
14. Sir Francis Drake
15. "Hail to the Chief"

Page 24

1. the nervous system
2. Halley's comet
3. solid, liquid, and gas
4. a barometer
5. smog
6. the elbow
7. chlorophyll
8. kinetic energy
9. an earthquake
10. a carnivore
11. oxygen
12. hot
13. the esophagus
14. meteors
15. a crater

Page 25

1. no
2. 300
3. having the same size and shape
4. They weigh the same.
5. CLXXVI
6. a protractor
7. 5
8. 144
9. ten
10. 3/4
11. nine
12. obtuse
13. yes
14. a straight line
15. an ordinal number

ANSWER KEY (cont.)

Page 26
1. Harriet B. Stowe
2. a thesaurus
3. conjunctions
4. imperative
5. guide words
6. author, subject, and title
7. Huck Finn
8. a vampire
9. heading, inside address, greeting, body, closing, and signature
10. alliteration
11. homophones
12. in a subway station
13. to sign your name
14. humble
15. nonfiction

Page 27
1. Mt. Everest
2. redwood tree
3. Sears Tower
4. blue whale
5. North American ostrich
6. Asia
7. Greenland
8. anaconda
9. African bush elephant
10. killer whale
11. cheetah
12. peregrine falcon

Page 28
1. 1
2. 2
3. 5
4. 32
5. 90
6. 100
7. 4
8. 0
9. 110
10. 360
11. 206
12. 144
13. 14
14. 52
15. 64
16. 100
17. 366
18. 500
19. 88
20. 11

Page 29
1. 8 sides
2. 102
3. Oklahoma
4. 3rd president
5. Picasso
6. Quebec
7. 13
8. 10 sides
9. 12 months
10. tambourine
11. cumulus
12. Sacramento
13. 24 hours

14. 100 years
15. over 600
16. May

Page 30
1. late date
2. fat rat
3. bad lad
4. rude dude
5. bug's mug (or bug mug)
6. long song
7. fat cat
8. double trouble
9. big pig
10. Swiss miss
11. bony pony
12. bright light
13. funny bunny
14. glad lad
15. lazy daisy
16. sad dad
17. mouse house
18. no dough
19. cross boss
20. funny money

Page 31
1. self-service
2. coauthor
3. ups and downs
4. absentminded
5. light-footed
6. weather bureau
7. nonexistent
8. three fifths
9. roller skates
10. warm-blooded
11. ice cream
12. all ready
13. ad-lib or ad lib
14. jack-o'-lantern
15. eighty-five
16. up-to-date
17. autobiography
18. drive-in

Page 32
1. desert
2. capital
3. thorough
4. anyway
5. effect
6. imply
7. latter
8. angel
9. illicit
10. disprove
11. stationery
12. accept
13. proceed
14. preposition
15. quit

Page 33
1. noon
2. did
3. ewe
4. Bob

5. tot
6. peep
7. eye
8. pop or dad
9. dud
10. toot
11. bib
12. solos
13. mom or mum
14. kayak
15. level
16. pop
17. Answers will vary. They include Anna, Eve, Hannah, and Nan.
18. pup
19. deed
20. civic

Page 34
1. absent without leave
2. repondez s'il vous plait (please reply)
3. Mothers Against Drunk Driving
4. prisoner of war
5. recreational vehicle
6. United Nations International Children's Emergency Fund
7. tender loving care
8. government issue
9. Special Weapons and Tactics
10. cash on delivery
11. bacon, lettuce, and tomato
12. intelligence quotient
13. rest in peace
14. as soon as possible
15. Thank goodness (God) it's Friday!

Page 35
1. telephone
2. champion
3. gasoline
4. veterinarian or veteran
5. popular
6. bicycle
7. airplane
8. tuxedo
9. mathematics
10. referee
11. automobile
12. refrigerator
13. submarine
14. promenade
15. gymnastics or gymnasium
16. taxicab
17. hamburger
18. spectacles
19. limousine
20. examination

ANSWER KEY *(cont.)*

Page 36
1. Boise
2. several
3. almost
4. sturdy
5. dynamite
6. teal
7. alpaca
8. cashew
9. ewe
10. Wednesday
11. aye
12. yellow
13. owlet
14. et cetera
15. radish
16. shanty
17. tyke
18. kettledrum
19. umbrella
20. lance

Page 37
Answers will vary.

Page 38
anywhere
baseball
campground
downtown
eyelid
flagpole
grandfather
handshake
inside
lighthouse
junkyard
mailbox
northeast
overcome
paintbrush
quarterback
railroad
seaport
textbook
underline

Page 39
different
condition
prisoner
medicine
radium
aspirin
informal
settlement
vitamins
guarantee
limousine
earliest
bravery
overtone
important

Page 40
1. sharp
2. shark
3. share

4. care
5. chart
6. charm
7. hard
8. hare
9. fare
10. farm
11. alarm
12. lark
13. bark
14. dark
15. dare
16. date
17. late
18. lane
19. cane
20. cone
21. done

Page 41
1. Q
2. XTC
3. NME
4. NV
5. B
6. O
7. SA
8. EZ
9. J
10. CU
11. AT
12. C
13. O
14. XL
15. DK

Page 42
1. dam + pen = dampen
2. sea + son = season
3. cot + ton = cotton
4. pea + nut = peanut
5. sun + dry = sundry
6. son + net = sonnet
7. off + ice = office
8. rat + tan = rattan
9. men + ace = menace
10. Jack + son = Jackson

Page 43
1. Golden Gate
2. brownie
3. violet, rose, iris, or bluebells
4. bluebird
5. greenhorn
6. orange
7. pinkeye, or black death
8. yellow jacket
9. Greyhound
10. blackboard
11. whitewall
12. red meat
13. Purple Heart
14. Blackbeard

Page 44
1. cornucopia
2. cornerstone
3. corner

4. corned beef
5. corncob
6. corncrib
7. cornerback
8. corn oil
9. cornet
10. corny
11. cornea
12. cut corners
13. cornstarch
14. cornice
15. cornflakes

Page 45
1. fare
2. farm team
3. farm hand
4. farrow
5. farther
6. farmer
7. faraway
8. farewell
9. farthing
10. far-fetched
11. Far East
12. so far so good
13. farce
14. to go too far
15. far-reaching

Page 46
1. Peter
2. petrified
3. petal
4. carpet
5. repetitious
6. puppet
7. petite
8. petunia
9. petticoat
10. petroleum
11. petty officer
12. petty cash
13. petition
14. petri dish
15. petit four

Page 47
1. shore
2. forefather
3. galore
4. Oregon
5. swore
6. forefinger
7. chore
8. snore
9. oregano
10. adore
11. forecast
12. forest
13. more
14. carnivores
15. ignore

ANSWER KEY *(cont.)*

Page 48
1. thermos
2. thereabouts
3. mathematics
4. thermometer
5. theme song
6. gather
7. theft
8. thesaurus
9. thesis
10. bathe
11. theory
12. then
13. panther
14. weather
15. theater

Page 49
1. praying mantis
2. mango
3. mantel
4. manger
5. Manitoba
6. manufacture
7. many
8. mandarin
9. mandolin
10. manicure
11. manhole
12. manager
13. mansion
14. manhandle
15. mannequin

Page 50
Women
1. Pearl S. Buck
2. Helen Keller
3. Eleanor Roosevelt
4. Clara Barton
5. Jane Addams
6. Amelia Earhart
7. Laura Ingalls Wilder
8. Susan B. Anthony
9. Harriet Tubman
10. Sally Ride
Deserts
1. Black Rock
2. Syrian
3. Libyan
4. Death Valley
5. Negav
6. Sahara
7. Great Sandy
8. Mojave
9. Sonoran
10. Gobi

Page 51
U.S. Landmarks
1. Mount Saint Helens
2. Grand Canyon
3. Pearl Harbor
4. Mount Rushmore
5. Mount McKinley
6. Gateway Arch
7. White House
8. Plymouth Rock
9. Statue of Liberty
10. Old Faithful
Explorers
1. Byrd
2. Balboa
3. Cabot
4. Ponce de Leon
5. Alexander the Great
6. Vespucci
7. Columbus
8. Lewis and Clark
9. Coronado
10. Cartier

Page 52
Clouds
1. stratocumulus
2. cumulonimbus
3. altocumulus
4. nimbostratus
5. stratus
6. cirrostratus
7. cumulus
8. cirrus
9. altostratus
North American Nations
1. Bahamas
2. Canada
3. Guatemala
4. Mexico
5. El Salvador
6. United States
7. Costa Rica
8. Jamaica
9. Cuba

Page 53
Answers will vary.

Page 54
Answers will vary.

Page 55
1. tease
2. stand
3. aunt
4. need
5. attend
6. ten
7. test
8. sun
9. ate
10. taste
11. sand
12. sea
13. unite
14. tent
15. den
16. tuna
17. sunset
18. seat
19. tune
20. end

Page 56
1. waste
2. is a penny earned
3. catches the worm
4. the mice will play
5. before they hatch
6. what you can do today
7. in the mouth
8. you leap
9. flock together
10. make a man healthy, wealthy, and wise

Page 57
The grass is always greener on the other side.
1. eggs
2. hide
3. these
4. lone
5. sorry
6. koala
7. rather
8. new
9. toss

Page 58
You can if you think you can.
1. F
2. O
3. N
4. H
5. A
6. U
7. Y
8. C
9. T
10. K
11. I

Page 59
1. opportunity
2. butterfly
3. blizzard
4. intelligence
5. innocent
6. wiggle
7. vacuum
8. moon
9. doodle
10. pessimist
11. borrow
12. giraffe
13. gaggle
14. football
15. buccaneer
16. syllable
17. sorrow
18. bazaar
19. exaggerate
20. pennant

ANSWER KEY *(cont.)*

Page 60
1. Antarctica
2. dividend
3. abracadabra
4. exercise
5. episode
6. critic
7. blurb
8. arena
9. surplus
10. classic
11. moonbeam
12. lentil
13. tolerant
14. penmanship
15. aqua
16. register
17. millennium

Page 61

Answers will vary.

Page 62

Answers will vary.

Page 63

Answers will vary.

Page 64

Answers will vary.

Page 65

Answers will vary.

Page 66

Answers will vary. Here are a few:
auctioned
housemaid
reputation
equation
pneumonia
discourage
ultraviolet
ambidextrous

Page 67
1. niece
2. hungry
3. library
4. hearing
5. December
6. large
7. belt
8. vine
9. green
10. head
11. calf
12. dawn
13. book
14. captain
15. ceiling
16. room (or house)
17. girl
18. curtain
19. bird
20. water (or lake, ocean, or river)

Page 68

1. a daisy
2. silk
3. a hornet
4. a whistle
5. an ox
6. a peacock
7. pie
8. a lark
9. a pin
10. a sheet or snow
11. a wink
12. a beet
13. a ghost
14. an eel
15. molasses in January

Page 69

Answers will vary slightly.
1. enjoys telling stories
2. his father became firm in his discipline
3. if she was getting scared
4. that she was astonished or mesmerized
5. that she would be leaving
6. that he had no information about what was happening
7. "Stay where you are."
8. that she slept soundly
9. that she was ill
10. that he would be in trouble

Page 70
1. H
2. A
3. S
4. A
5. S
6. A
7. H
8. S
9. S
10. S
11. H
12. S
13. A
14. S
15. H
16. A
17. S
18. A
19. S
20. H

Page 71

Answers will vary slightly.
1. do something to someone else knowing that it is to one's own detriment
2. to treat with contempt or scorn
3. to win by a small margin
4. to make someone feel slighted
5. to interfere
6. to go straight ahead
7. to pay an exorbitant price
8. in plain sight
9. to treat with scorn
10. exactly

Page 72

Answers will vary slightly.
1. to believe only in part
2. peppy, active, or ready to go
3. to earn an income
4. person or thing that is cherished
5. to create or to prepare falsely
6. humiliation
7. calm
8. a show-off in sports
9. to talk frankly
10. to overact
11. a bad person
12. lavishly
13. full of nonsense
14. the basics
15. to destroy one's plan or one's reputation

Page 73
1. foot
2. back
3. skin; bones
4. lip
5. hands
6. teeth
7. heart
8. eye; eye
9. belly
10. neck
11. ear
12. wrist
13. limb
14. throat
15. head; shoulders

Page 74

Animal	Male	Female	Young	Group
fox	dog	vixen	cub	skulk
chicken	rooster	hen	chick	flock
lion	lion	lioness	cub	pride
cattle	bull	cow	calf	herd
whale	bull	cow	calf	herd
seal	bull	cow	pup	herd
ostrich	cock	hen	chick	flock
sheep	ram	ewe	lamb	flock
goose	gander	goose	gosling	gaggle
kangaroo	buck	doe	joey	herd
hog	boar	sow	piglet	herd
goat	billy	nanny	kid	herd